peh-peh-peh-penguin face

GUS & WALDO
CRAZY IN LOVE

by
Massimo Fenati

First published in hardback in Great Britain
in 2010 by Orion Books, an imprint of the Orion
Publishing Group Ltd, Orion House,
5 Upper St Martin's Lane, London, WC2H 9EA
An Hachette UK Company

A CIP catalogue record for this book is available
from the British Library.

ISBN: 978 1 4091 3106 9

Printed and bound in Spain

The Orion Publishing Group's policy is to use papers
that are natural, renewable and recyclable and made
from wood grown in sustainable forests. The logging
and manufacturing processes are expected to
conform to the environmental regulations
of the country of origin.

Every effort has been made to fulfil the requirements
with regard to reproducing copyright material. The
author and publisher will be glad to rectify any
omissions at the earliest opportunity.

www.orionbooks.co.uk
www.gusandwaldo.com

Thanks to:
Lisa Milton, Amanda Harris, Jane Sturrock,
Sian Rees, Simon Trewin, Walter Iuzzolino
and everybody at Orion

for Marta and Fabio

This book is a compendium of Gus & Waldo's Book of Fame and Gus & Waldo's Book of Sex. Here we share their tales of Penguin Love as one.

Love is blind, love is kind, love is for all mankind. Trust us, our friend, this is what we recommend. Penguins mate for life, and true love should just run rife!

Gus and Waldo are in love

And they do it all the time

They do it so much

Their life is super whoopie doo!

Everything they do,
they do together

They just
DON'T

DO IT

anymore

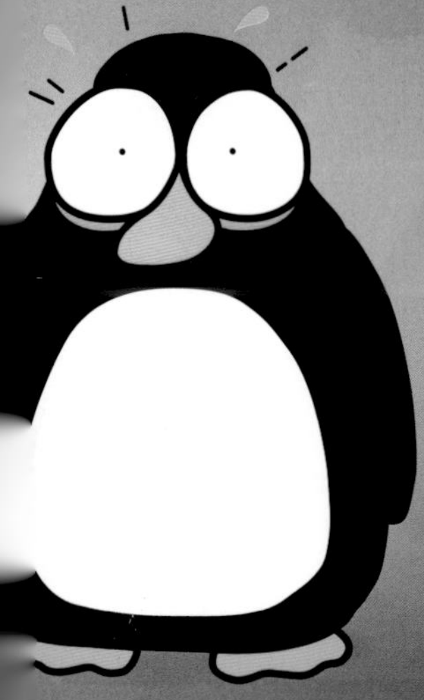

the other feels booky

Time to recapture the passion

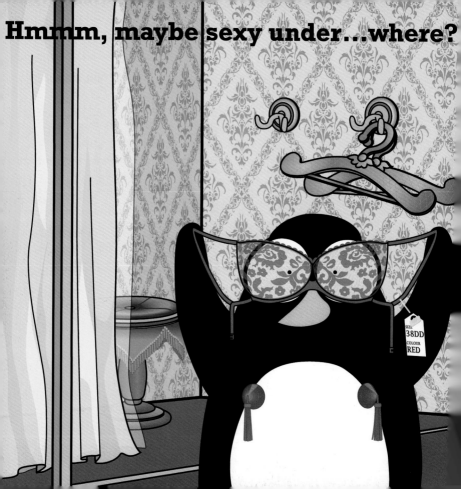

Hippy Hippo's advice

But the wrong gadget wi

go down like a lead balloon

Trust Randy the rat:
shoe fetish is where it's at!

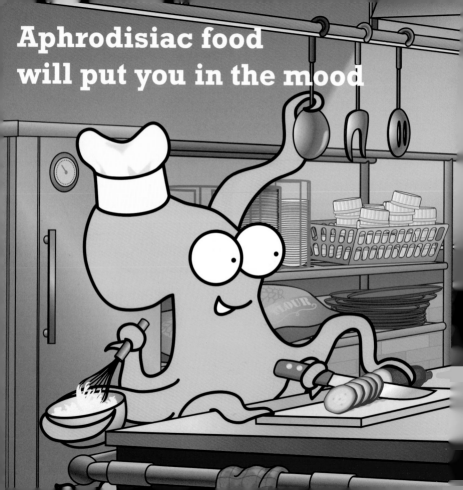

A 'ménage à trois'? ...

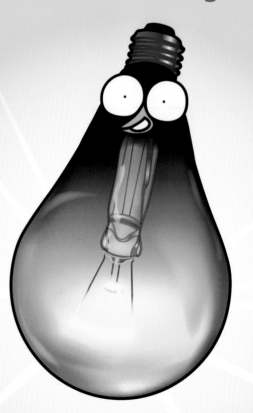

That's a brilliant idea!

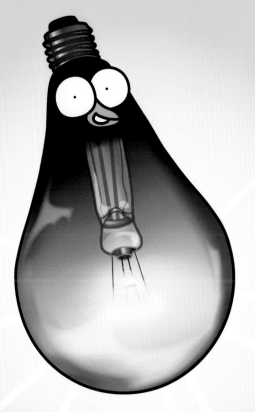

Oh!...
That's what it meant!

You are cordially invited to
Gus and Waldo's
swinger's party
on Saturday 22

Booze and nibbles will be provided
(Un)dress casual

They eye them all: too big, too small ...

... too squishy ... too spiky ...

too fluffy... too bitey...

But who's this stranger in the dark

giving me such fire and spark?

Penguins mate for life

So Gus and Waldo set of

o live happily ever after

Time passes by,

but one thing never changes...

They love Love
so much...

...that they want
the whole world
to love them

In their quest for fame

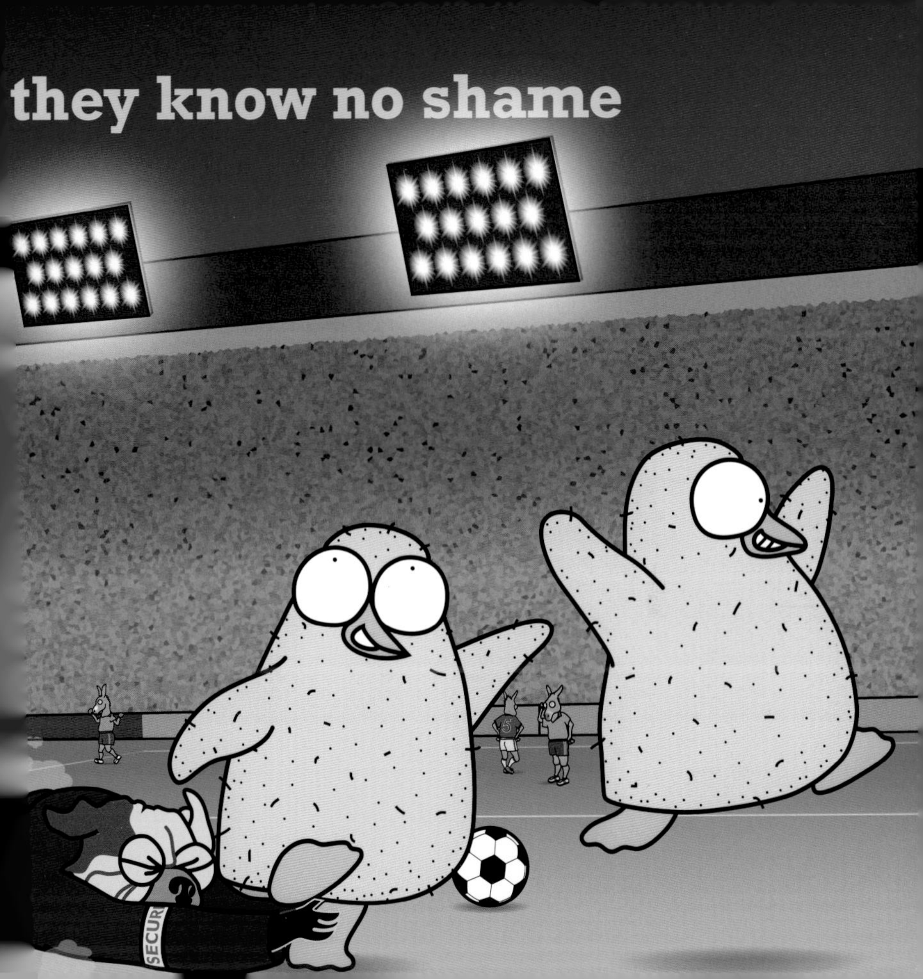
they know no shame

...they show the world their love

Fame is a roof
over your head

Fame is making

Fame is bein

ords of the bling

Gus as agent James Bonk 00¹/₇

in

LICENCE TO CHILL

A UNITED BEASTS PRODUCTION IN ASSOCIATION WITH ANTARCTIC SCREEN. GUS WALDO IN "LICENCE TO CHILL" SCREENPLAY JOHN SMITH PHOTOGRAPHY PINCO PALLINO
CAST ANNA GIOVANNA EDITOR RUFUS ASHWORTH COSTUMES INIER IDER MUSIC THOMAS THOMSON VISUALS PIPPO SEMOLA SCENOGRAPHY CRILLO LOVIO SOUND DRAMA WILLIAM ZIZZY
EDITOR CHICO BRIGOLA PRODUCER RAVIOLO FIFFY DIRECTOR OF PHOTOGRAPHY PRENDO ASSLESS WRITTEN AND DIRECTED BY EGG YOUTZY

GUS
WALDO

FROM AWARD WINNING DIRECTOR ANG EEL

BROKEBEAK MOUNTAIN

IN ASSOCIATION WITH JAMIE COMPANY JELECTION COMPANY
GUS WALDO IN "BROKEBEAK MOUNTAIN" HEATH BADOCLE JAKE KILDERMANN
PHOTOGRAPHY TOM LOCK II PRODUCTION MUSIC AL LAMPE COSTUMES JOHN STITCH DIRECTOR PINCO PALLINO
MUSIC ANNA LA MAMMA EDITOR RUFUS LA BISKOLA COSTUMES INGER IDE SOUND PINO ANNIELLO
SCENERY THOMAS TH CHRILLA MUSIC CRILLO LOVIO SOUND WILLIAM ZIZZY EDITOR CHICO BRIGOLA

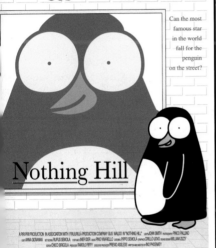

GUS   WALDO

Can the most
famous star
in the world
fall for the
penguin
on the street?

Nothing Hill

A PRII PRII PRODUCTION IN ASSOCIATION WITH FRIULARULA PRODUCTION COMPANY GUS WALDO IN "NOTHING HILL" LIGHTING JOHN SMITH PHOTOGRAPHY PINCO PALLINO MUSIC ANNA GIOVANNA COSTUME RUFUS SEMOLA EDITING INDER IDER MUSIC PINO VIVARELLO EXECUTIVE PIPPO SEMOLA CATERING CIRILLO UOVO SOUND DESIGN WILLIAM ZIZZY EDITOR CHICO BRIGOLA EXECUTIVE PRODUCER PRENDO ASSILEEG WRITTEN AND DIRECTED BY INO PHOENIXXY

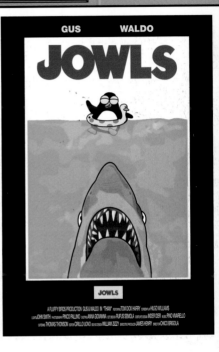

GUS   WALDO

JOWLS

JOWLS

A FLUFFY BIRDS PRODUCTION GUS & WALDO IN "THAW" FEATURING TOM DICK HARRY SCREENPLAY HUGO WILLIAMS LIGHTING JOHN SMITH PHOTOGRAPHY PINCO PALLINO CASTING ANNA GIOVANNA SET DESIGN RUFUS SEMOLA COSTUME DESIGN INDER IDER MUSIC PINO VIVARELLO CATERING THOMAS THOMSON EDITOR CIRILLO UOVO SOUND DESIGN WILLIAM ZIZZY EXECUTIVE PRODUCER JAMES HENRY DIRECTOR CHICO BRIGOLA

Fame is plastic, paper and gold

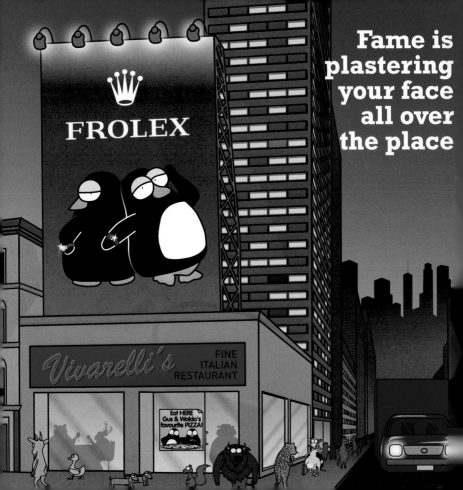

Fame is being back after the break

TROUT
WITH POTATOES
SOUP

MACKEREL
SOUP

HERRING
WITH VEGETABLES
SOUP

OCTOPUS
IN OCTOPUS STOCK
SOUP

SALMON
SOUP

SQUID
WITH VEGETABLES
SOUP

COLEY
IN TOMATO JUICE
SOUP

HALIBUT
. WITH CARROTS AND ONIONS
SOUP

COD
WITH BROWN RICE
SOUP

SPICY
PRAWN
SOUP

TUNA
WITH VEGETABLES AND

Fame is stardom

Fame is fashion fever

Fame is being

Fame is avoidin

Fame is having to

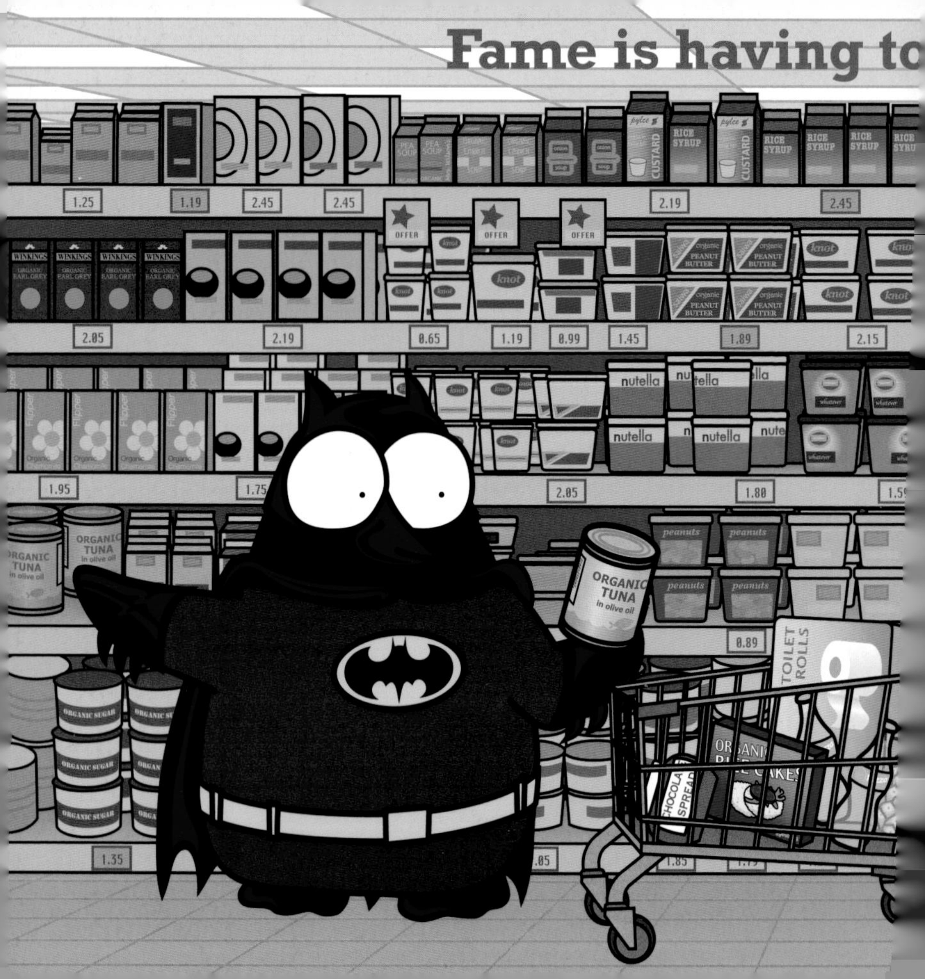

shop in disguise

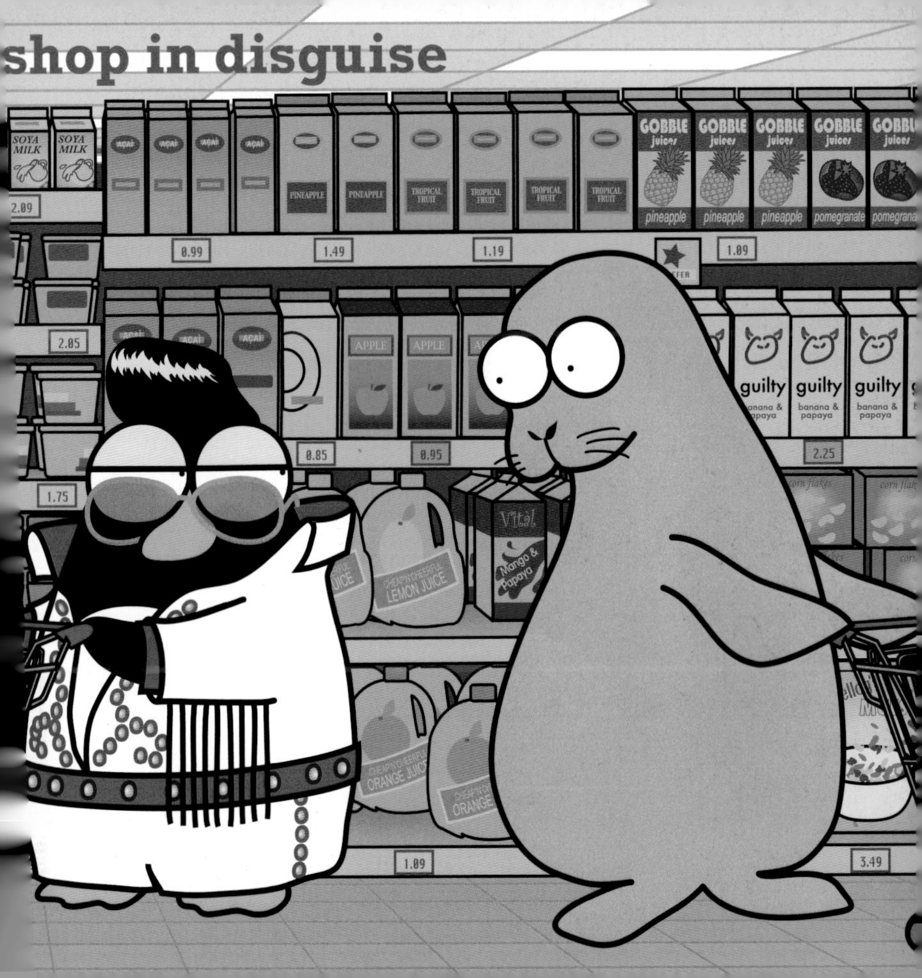

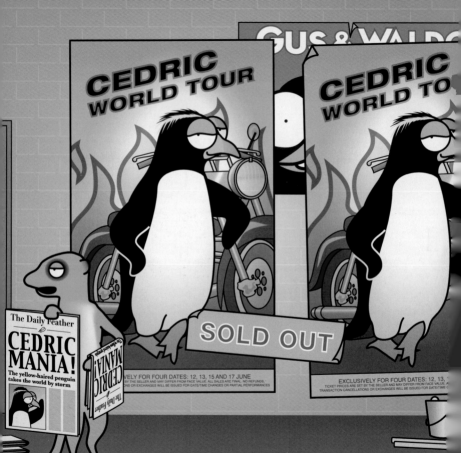

The New

Scandal! Gus & Waldo in Huge Coke and Cocoa Binge

'We're addicted to fizzy drinks' admit the couple. Tax evasion and money laundering used to finance their perverse addiction. Millions of fans in tears.

In the early hours of Sunday morning, Gus and Waldo, the celebrity penguin couple, were found in what has been described as "an infernal mass of Coke cans and chocolate boxes" in their hotel room. Police were alerted by hotel staff, as guests at the hotel could hear loud munching and gurgling noises all through the night. After getting no reply from the penguins, the

admitted their addiction. "It all started when we read that chocolate releases endorphins and that the caffeine in Coke gives you a kick" said Waldo. "The celebrity lifestyle can be quite demanding and we needed a boost every so often. But now things got out of flippers".

Their PR agent, Max Nifford, was unavailable for comment.

The spokesman for the Coca Loca company denied any allegation of their soft drink having addictive effects, but stated that the company was "delighted Gus and Waldo chose our brand for their binge in what has been a tremendous year for our business".

But the penguins' year has been far from tremendous, they

ork Times

25 June 200[?]

do in their hotel room yesterday. "But chocolate releases end[...]

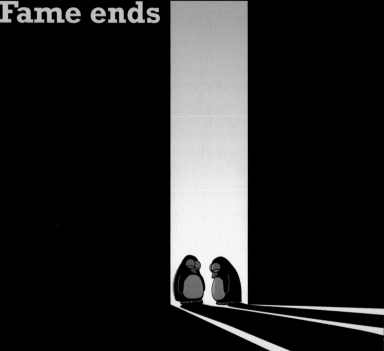

Fame ends

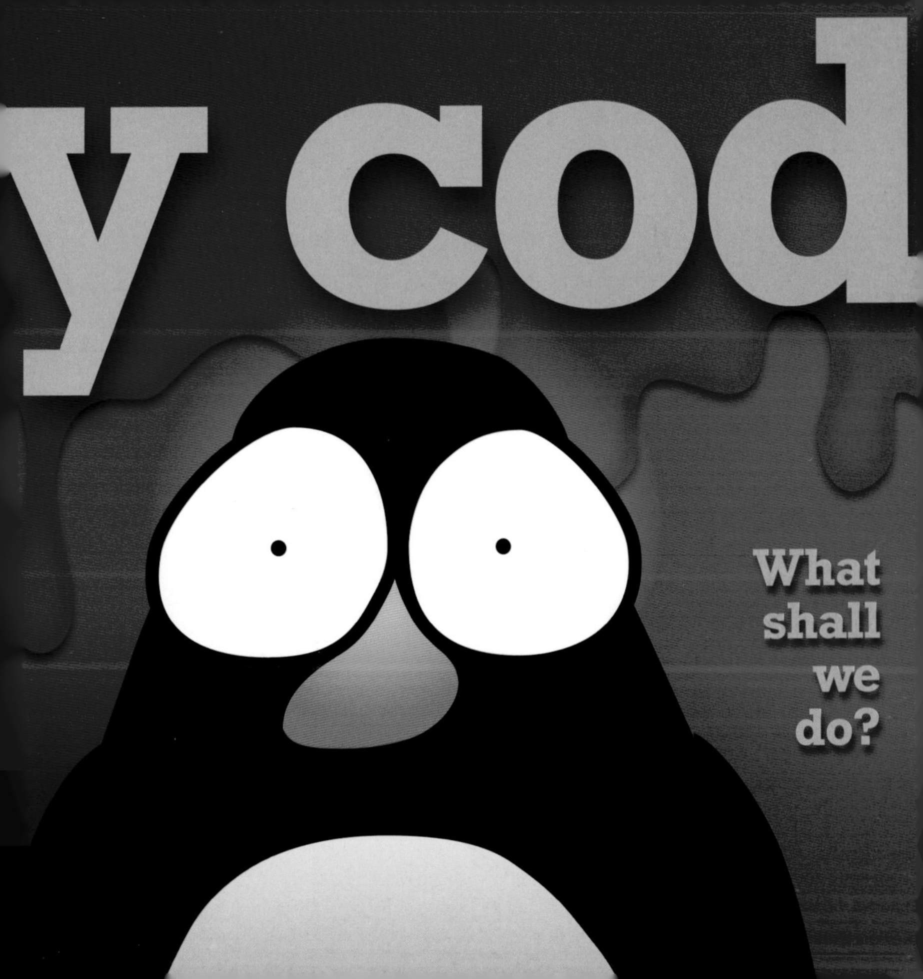
y cod
What shall we do?

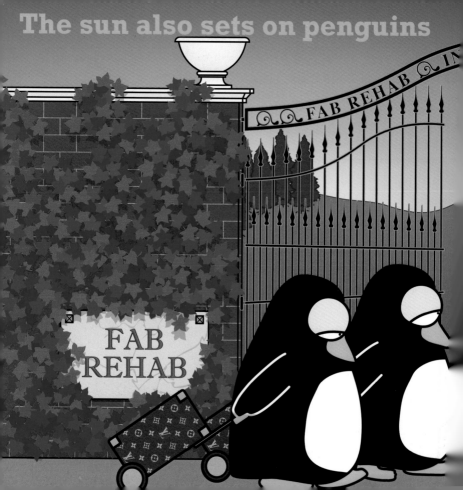

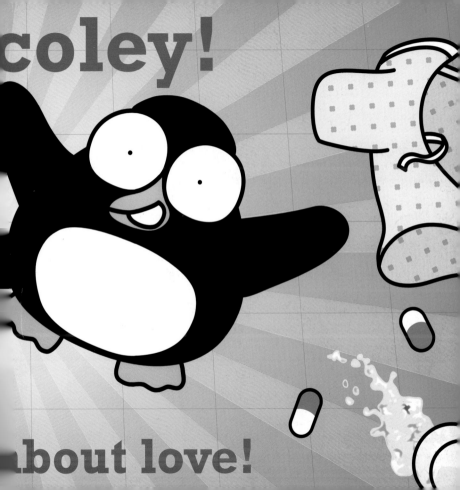